M000086786

Guitar
Initial

Pieces
including Duets
for Trinity College London exams

2016-2019

Published by
Trinity College London
www.trinitycollege.com

Registered in England
Company no. 02683033
Charity no. 1014792

Printed in England by Caligraving Ltd.

Allemande

Michael Praetorius
(1571-1621)

Time to dance ♩ = 108–112

Mi chacra

Traditional Argentine

Proudly ♩ = 104–110

* Tap lightly on the guitar.

The Water is Wide

arr. Nicholas Powlesland

Traditional

Hill and Gully Rider

Traditional Jamaican

Andante ♩ = 84–90

Shine Like a Star

Traditional Urdu

With hope ♩ = 96–100

The Cuckoo

arr. Lee Sollory

Traditional Swiss

Play the repeat in the exam.

Long, Long Ago

Thomas Haynes Bayly
(1797-1839)

Luna

Frédéric Costantino
(b. 1971)

6

Night Night, Knight

(the battle is won and the day is done)

Nick Walker & James Longworth

Showtime

Nicholas Powlesland
(b. 1965)

Saltarello

Peter Nuttall
(b. 1949)

Chim Chim Cher-ee

Richard M. Sherman and Robert B. Sherman

Tika Taka

Lee Sollory
(b. 1959)